THIS BOOK
BELONGS TO

....

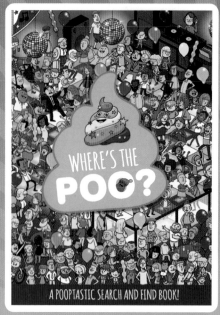
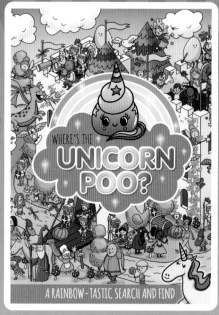
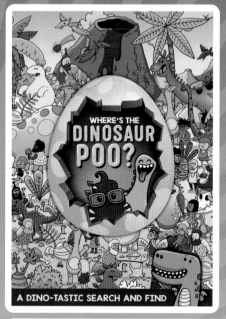
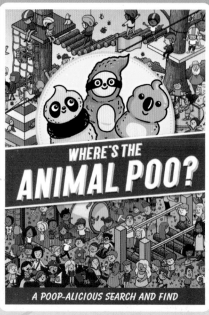

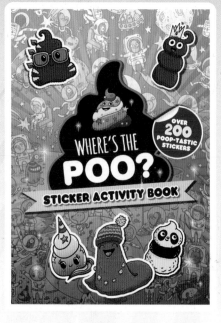

WHERE'S THE PENGUIN POO?

ORCHARD

MEET THE POOS

These super-cool poos love an adventure and can be found chilling all over the world. Spot them ice skating, at a winter market, on the ski slopes and anywhere there's fun to be had!

PIP

is the regal emperor penguin poo. He rules the ice and snow.

POLLY

the polar bear poo looks cute but beware her ferocious roar if you get too close.

GREAT SKATES

The pao pals are excited to try ice skating for the very first time. Can you spot them slipping and sliding among the skaters?

ARCTIC ADVENTURE

Brrrr! The poos are visiting their friends at the icy North Pole. Can you find them hiding among the Arctic animals?

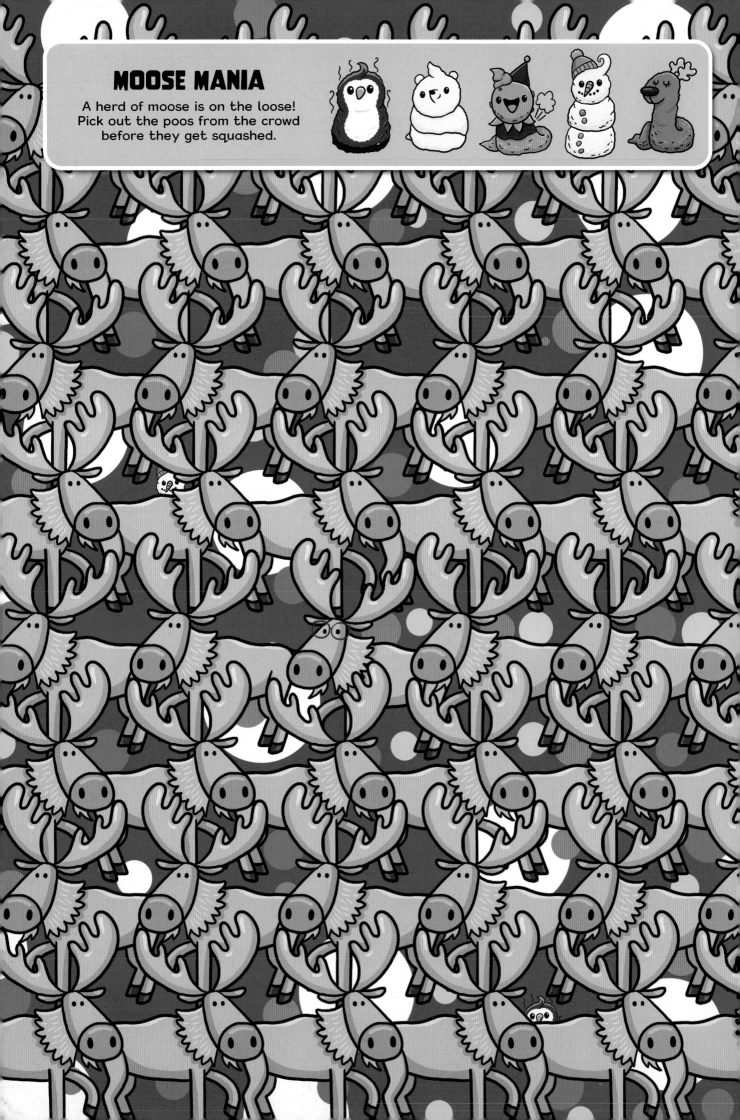

MOOSE MANIA

A herd of moose is on the loose!
Pick out the poos from the crowd
before they get squashed.

ODD ONE OUT!

Can you spot the moose that looks different to the others?

HAPPY CAMPERS

The poo friends are enjoying a camping trip in the great outdoors – they love the fresh air! Can you spot the poos relaxing?

FESTIVE MARKET

Eddie the elf poo is shopping for presents at the winter market! Find him and his poo pals among the food stalls and colourful lights.

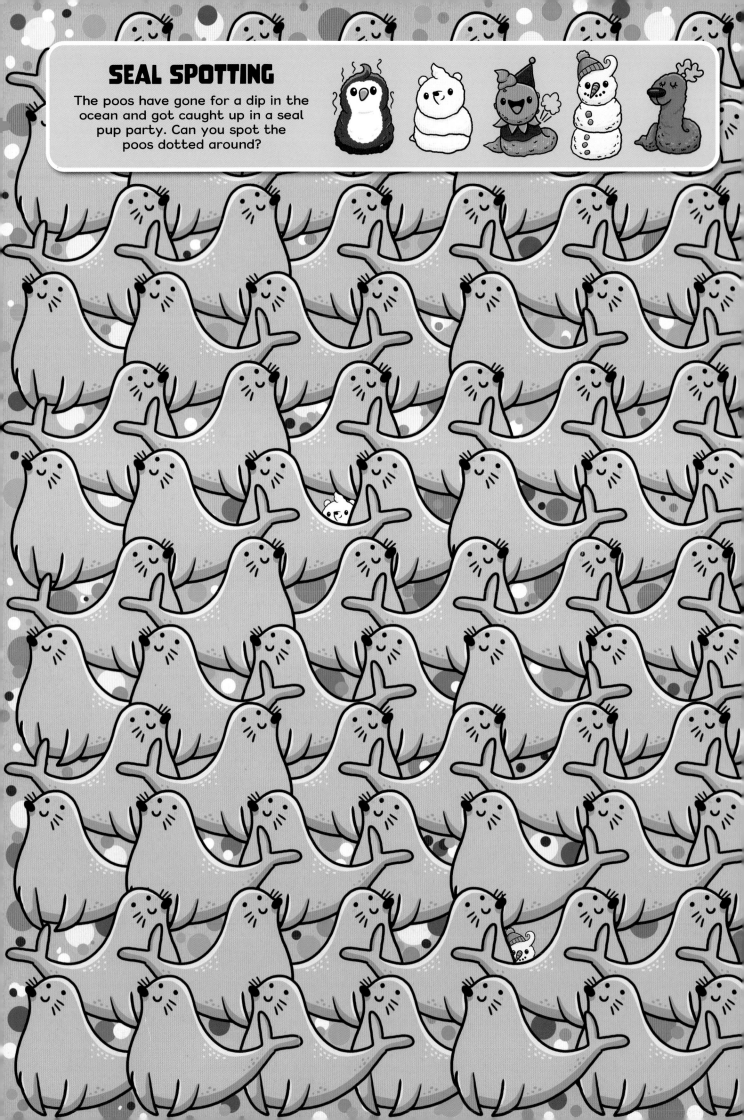

SEAL SPOTTING

The poos have gone for a dip in the ocean and got caught up in a seal pup party. Can you spot the poos dotted around?

ODD ONE OUT!

There's one seal that looks a bit different to the others. Can you find it?

FROZEN FAIRY TALE

Snowy loves visiting the frozen fairy-tale castle – his favourite story is Snow White, of course! Find the poos in the magical scene.

TASTY TREATS

The poos all have a sweet tooth! Can you find them before they gobble up all the delicious treats in Candyland?

FOXY FUN

The poos have made friends with a family of Arctic foxes. Can you find Pip and the other poos hiding among them?

ODD ONE OUT!

One Arctic fox looks different to the rest. Can you spot which one?

MOUNTAIN MISCHIEF

Wheee! Ruby the reindeer poo is skiing down the mountain at top speed. Find all the poos on the slopes before they whizz past.

TRAMPOLINE PARK

Boing! Boing! How high can Polly and her friends bounce? Try spotting all the playful poos as they jump up and down.

WRAP UP

The poos are helping Snowy pick out a new woolly hat. Find the poos before they get lost in the pile.

ODD ONE OUT!

Three of these woolly items aren't quite like the rest. Can you spot which ones?

READING CORNER

Pip enjoys reading and is looking for a good detective story. Can you help solve the mystery of where the poos are hiding in the library?

PREHISTORIC POO

The poos have slipped back in time to the past. Can you spot the poos among the prehistoric animals? Watch out for sabre-tooth tigers!

ANSWERS

Now try and find the extra items hidden in each scene.

GREAT SKATES

A man with a tray ☐

A girl on her phone ☐

A pregnant lady with a pink T-shirt ☐

Three ice hockey players ☐

Five penguin skating aids ☐

Two girls in pink tutus ☐

Six red mugs ☐

One bear skating aid ☐

A bowl of cutlery ☐

A woman with a broken leg ☐

ARCTIC ADVENTURE

A snowman with a top hat ☐

Two animals in a rubber ring ☐

Three people in the water ☐

A grey baby penguin ☐

An Arctic fox with armbands ☐

A penguin on a diving board ☐

A bucket of fish ☐

Nine penguin eggs ☐

A red door ☐

Four walruses ☐

MOOSE MANIA

HAPPY CAMPERS

- A bear ☐
- A cat in a tree ☐
- A bird pooing ☐
- Five children toasting marshmallows ☐
- A man collecting wood ☐
- A man with binoculars ☐
- A squirrel with a marshmallow ☐
- A family playing cards ☐
- A man pumping up an airbed ☐
- Two rolls of toilet paper ☐

FESTIVE MARKET

- Two bananas ☐
- Ten candy canes ☐
- A toy mouse ☐
- Roasted chestnuts ☐
- An owl ☐
- Ketchup and mustard ☐
- Two pink presents ☐
- Four red ribbons ☐
- Two people wearing reindeer antlers ☐
- Someone dressed as Father Christmas ☐

SEAL SPOTTING

FROZEN FAIRY TALE

- Humpty Dumpty ☐
- Three witches ☐
- A genie's lamp ☐
- Six mice wearing handkerchiefs ☐
- Eight gold coins ☐
- A girl licking a lollipop ☐
- Little Red Riding Hood ☐
- A man looking through a telescope ☐
- A wizard ☐
- Rapunzel ☐

TASTY TREATS

- Eight sweets with red spots ☐
- A penguin in a purple hat ☐
- Three hearts ☐
- Three green and white candy canes ☐
- Two penguins with yellow hats ☐
- Eight cherries ☐
- Two straws ☐
- A green door ☐
- A purple jellybean ☐
- A cupcake with blue icing ☐

FOXY FUN

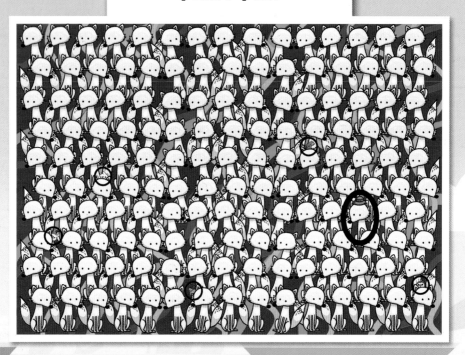

MOUNTAIN MISCHIEF

A pile of snowballs ☐

A yeti ☐

A dog with earmuffs ☐

Four green skimobiles ☐

A man wearing a white helmet ☐

A cat ☐

Two birds ☐

A snowman ☐

Nine red flags ☐

A skier crossing the finishing line ☐

TRAMPOLINE PARK

A man drinking a bottle of water ☐

Two apple juice cartons ☐

A red woolly hat ☐

A girl with a heart on her T-shirt ☐

Six beach balls ☐

A woman with a sling ☐

A man with a broken arm ☐

A red foam finger ☐

Four teddy bears ☐

A man with an eye patch ☐

WRAP UP

Did you find me? If you're stuck, take another look at the Camping Trip.

READING CORNER

Two librarians shushing people ☐

A snow globe ☐

A man carrying five books ☐

A book about a unicorn ☐

A mouse with some cheese ☐

A white sock ☐

A man dressed as a pirate ☐

A girl with blonde pigtails ☐

A cat reading a book ☐

A man watering a plant ☐

PREHISTORIC POO

Two spotty handkerchiefs ☐

Five starfish ☐

Twelve sloths ☐

Two bears wearing glasses ☐

Two grey squirrels with sticks ☐

Four eagles ☐

A red feather ☐

Two pink eels ☐

Two laughing sabre-tooth tigers ☐

Four red squirrels holding acorns ☐

ORCHARD BOOKS
First published in Great Britain in 2021 by The Watts Publishing Group © 2021 The Watts Publishing Group Limited
Illustrations by Dynamo Limited   Additional images © Shutterstock
A CIP catalogue record for this book is available from the British Library
ISBN 978 1 40836 628 8   Printed and bound in China   1 3 5 7 9 10 8 6 4 2

Orchard Books, an imprint of Hachette Children's Group
Part of The Watts Publishing Group Limited, Carmelite House, 50 Victoria Embankment, London, EC4Y 0DZ
An Hachette UK Company   www.hachette.co.uk   www.hachettechildrens.co.uk

FSC

MIX
Paper from responsible sources
FSC® C104740